C000071857

CLASSIFIED PULP NASTIES

BRUTE!

by

Malcolm Bennett
& Aidan Hughes

SPHERE BOOKS LIMITED
27 Wrights Lane, London W8 5TZ

First published in Great Britain by Sphere Books Limited

Copyright © 1984, 1985 & 1986
by Malcolm Bennett & Aidan Hughes
Published by Sphere Books Ltd 1987

TRADE
MARK

WARNING! Do not attempt to drive,
operate machinery or approach rutting livestock
whilst under the influence of this book.

Members and Genitalmen only

Set in Univers Bold Condensed and Extra-Bold 16pt
and Helvetica Bold Condensed 40pt

Printed and bound in Great Britain by
Cox & Wyman Ltd, Reading

To
US!

Contents

BROOKWOOD

ONCE upon a time there were three brothers, ROCKWOOD, THUD, and ELVIS THUG, and they lived in a wood by a brook. Brookwood Estate to be precise.

ONE day ROCKWOOD was being sick in the brook that ran by the wood, when he looked up and saw some men about their job.

ROCKWOOD thought, 'What's up?' and went over.

'Where's the foreman, lad?' ROCK-WOOD said, politely.

'In the pub with your kid, THUD.'

'Cor, our THUD with a PINT!' roared ROCKWOOD rushing off.

* * *

AT the pub THUD THUG and foreman BUD THUMP had a chat.

BUD THUMP looked at THUD THUG and said, 'Ay, THUD!'

'Wha!'

'Are you looking at my PINT?!!'

'BURP!!! YEAH! And it's your round,' replied THUD brutally. 'I've sucked mine dry like an old bag's GASH! And that's OFFICIAL!'

'OFFICIAL!' said BUD. 'But what about your kid, ELVIS, the site is short of muscle and needs good lads like him. But not that ROCKWOOD twat, he's as daft as a tap!'

Then ROCKWOOD burst into the pub!

'Cor, a **PINT!** I'll have that, mate!' barked ROCKWOOD THUG laughing.

'That's our kid,' chuckled THUD as ROCKWOOD ploughed into the barmaid, 'he's a good 'un!'

* * *

THAT night ELVIS THUG and his computa bird DOT BLOCK were sat by the road laughing at traffic for kicks when ELVIS said, 'I love you, but you're a hag at that, what with all that snot on your snout like that.'

'MUCK OFF, GRID SLOBS!' bellowed a passing truck driver.

'Why don't you put a bog around that gob of yours, you ugly sack of pig!'

'DAMN YOUR SPERM FOR-EVER, KERB CRAP!' said a fat head at the wheel of a bus.

ELVIS shut up. But DOT was still laughing at the traffic.

'Cor, what a lark,' boffed DOT. 'I

haven't laughed so much since me and **JOCK BAGG** watched bread in sixty-eight!'

'BUTTON YER LIP, BURGER BRAIN, and get me down the PUB!'

'BOG OFF, SMOG SUCK-ERS!' roared a jag.

*   *   *

BACK at the 'Spud and Borstal' **THUD THUG** was going mad!

'Ay! Did you spill my **PINT?!!!**'

'Where's me kecks?' burped ROCK-WOOD from the deck.

'Who's been looking at my **PINT?!!!**' foreman **BUD THUMP** said again.

''Ere, PAT love, top up his **PINT** and give it here!' demanded ROCKWOOD.

''Ere's your ELVIS with a carcrash of a gash, lads, and what a monster at that!'

Barman:	'You can't park your car in here, mate. Especially a crashed car at that!'
Pub:	**'HA! HA!'**

A PINT!

Elvis:	'You can't talk to my bird like that, you odious beer bug!'
Dot:	'Here's my cash!'
Elvis:	'Yoink! **A TENNA!**'
Rockwood:	'Mine's a **PINT!**'
Thud:	'Did you spill my **PINT?!!**'
Rockwood:	'**BURP!! YEAH!!** Down me neck! Get 'em in!'
Bud Thump:	'Ay! ELVIS, do you want a few bob for six months graft?'
Elvis:	'What for? She's loaded!'
Dot:	'Get 'em in, ELVIS.'
Thud:	'**YOW!** Another **FIVA!!**'
Rockwood:	'I spilt his **PINT!**'

And all was good on the Brookwood Estate.

OFFICIAL!

THE CALL

Let me tell you the story of Wild Kid Wallasey and how he was in a pub when he got the Call. (Here I could tell you of how he drove his starving, snow-splattered dog team across the vast, deathlike wastes of Alaska; sailed and single-handedly navigated the treacherous Force Ten storms of the Oceans; clawed and fought his way up the sides of massive, wind-battered mountains; and how, without food, sleep, sweat or beer, crossed the burning, lifeless desert; wrestled live things to the ground with his own hands, captured an entire city and conquered one million squirming teenage nubiles, but it would take an entire hardback to describe his incredible adventure, so, to save you all the boring details, in the end he died).

The End

BLOKE-U-POKE!

Rock Buttock was a slut.

One day, when he was in Greaseby Bum Baths, a bloke saw his backeye. He said, 'That's a fine looking shit-chute you've got there, Rock. You could make a mint with your hole. Giz a go!'

'Okay,' said Rock, openly.

'Good!' said the bloke. 'Get your farting gear round **THIS!!!**' Then, hastily, the bloke shot his fist into Rock Buttock's bottom and wrenched it out again. Then, he blasted in another. When he punched his arm in again, he ripped out a pipe. A windpipe.

'Sorry,' the bloke said, putting it back.

'Forget it,' said Rock, grimacing.

YEEUCH!!!

The End

FORCE!

WHEN I got to the dump I was coshed. Pissed. Plastered. It was the drink.

I pitched out the Jag and piped the dump.

Squat. I aimed at the gaping hole of the doorway and headed for it.

Inside I stopped. Tearing back the mac, I wrenched the gleaming automatic shotgun from the leather harness strapped to my thigh.

WHOOF! a monster! I thrust its brutal snout into the dark of the hall.

Me, I can't stand poverty. With some people it's drunks. With me it's poor people. It's the smell: it makes me sick. This dump made me sick. It stank. Real bad. I nursed the hulking muzzle of the shotgun toward the foot of the stairs. I raced up them to the top.

Noise. Lights. Voices. People.

I checked the mechanism on the steel brute in my hands and tore into the first room. A mohican copped it first. The shot blasted him clear across the room.

The next punk backed. I let him. He saw the weapon. He saw its clean, broad snout. He saw the savage flared nostrils of the death hog aimed at his belly. He clenched his teeth, shut his eyes. I hissed. He shit. I squeezed the trigger.

The shotgun's fatal bark blew his back out. As he bounced and crumpled I whirled.

Punk three.

I was daft. He moved as I fired. I caught him on the hip. He went down, ruined. The wound lay blasted and raw against his black clothes like a steak in an undertaker's window. He spurted, splashing my Armani jacket near the cuff.

'**CATCH!**' I roared and, leaning over, let the gun shout in his ear. The Armani was fucked.

I knew there'd be panic in the other room. There was, and lots of it. Dopes stood plastered to every corner. As if they could hide from the brute!

A runt in the far corner moved. 'Ay you!' I thundered. 'Glue bag! Over 'ere!' I got a grip of his neck and dug in hard. My forehead ground into his. The hog nuzzled his throat.

It was violent. It was brutal. It was savage, vicious and inhuman. But it was fair. I bit him. Then again. He yelled. Then he yelled some more. I bit his nose and chin. I snapped at his lips and ears. I was like a wolf. Besides, blowing holes in people gets boring.

I stopped for a breather. The kid howled. So I dropped him. One of the other kids, a bearded boho type in a cap, inched forward.

I grabbed him. 'Where's the dope?!'

'It's behind you!'

I know what you're thinking. You're thinking: I bet he'll turn his back. You'd be right! I did. **THWACK!** The top of my nut caved in and my brain fell out. They kicked it. Then they kicked me in the clothes.

I sank back as another kick pounded my skull. **BOOM!** The gun went off blinding me, but I saw the kid drop, a hole gouged out of him.

I'd never fall for that one again.

The End

JOB'S NEW OVERALLS

Job dusted off his overalls and grinned. They were the best darned overalls he'd ever had. They were bright blue with pockets in every place where pockets could possibly be, and they had big red letters right across the back that said, 'ARM-STRONG'. They were the best overalls he'd ever had, and Job was making sure he kept them clean.

'I hear this is the first work you've done in seven years, huh, Job?'

Job squinted in the bright midday glare. 'Yup, it is,' he drawled, 'and then again, it ain't.'

Frank took the scruffy, work dirty Panama from his head and wiped his brow with his forearm. He spat into the dust. 'Looks to me like you're a might clean for a working man there, Job.'

Job looked down and scrutinised his bright blue overalls. 'Yup!' He danced, delighted. 'Looks to me like I'm as clean as a gizzard in a paper bag, and a damn sight drier too! Damned if I ain't!'

Frank glared at the shack beside the petrol pumps. 'C'mon, Job. I'll treat you to a beer.'

Job jumped slightly, the dust swirling lightly around his feet and settling on his sneakers. 'Hail!' went Job. 'Looks to me like I'm gonna have to be a might careful before I can jest swan right on over there and drink me a beer. Looks to me like my overalls'd be covered in shit before I was even two strides there!'

The End

CUB-COP!

It's a good laugh being a police dog, see. Take last week. Slobbering, I burst in this room, the lads in blue behind me. I barked. Instantly, these three punks left this big bag of coke and bolted. I leapt in and got a fucking good snort before the cops kicked me off. But it was worth it!

The End

FRANK!

It was cold. Icebergs are like that. I was cold. I lived on one. Alone. But then, I've always been alone...

   It all started when I woke up in the Lab and saw this hunch-back laughing at me. I knew then that things were bad. Then, when I found a mirror, it was worse.

I was eight-feet four in my diving boots, green, and had a bolt through my neck. When I came out of the Dole people would run up and shout, 'That's my leg!' or 'That's our kid's head you've got!' and things like that. It was embarrassing. It was true.

They all hated me. All of them, that is, but her. She was just a kid. She played with me. I let her. I killed her. Bad move, when you look like me.

Afterwards, I painstakingly rambled over to Germany to see my Dad, the Doc. He said, 'What's up, son?'

'I am. I'm twenty-eight blokes, Dad,' I slobbered, handing him a sack of bits. 'Make us a bird.'

'Not now, son,' Dad said, sewing a dick on my forehead. 'You're leaving.'

That's when he dumped me on this iceberg. Still, I get to eat fish twelve times a day and all the ice I can suck.

The End

WHEN MORNING WAS OVER

It was eight o'clock Monday morning and the factory hooter was blowing off. A thin mist was clearing over the rooftops of Greaseby as the first drops of rain fell earthward. In the doorway of a derelict pub Joe shivered and pulled the Harrington up around his neck. In five more minutes there would be no going back.

Joe dragged deep on his cigarette and watched the drizzle wet the narrow, cobbled streets that led to the factory gates. He hated this place. It'd been like a prison to him, and he'd served his time waiting for the courage to escape. And now he had it, and in just a few more minutes he would prove it.

He flicked his cigarette into the gutter as Harry Shipright peddled furiously into view.

'Mornin', Joe,' he called. 'Not going in today?'

'No, mate,' said Joe, defiantly. 'I'm gonna rob the wages van.'

'Give over, yer young bastard,' laughed Harry, cycling past. 'You'll be late n'all.'

Joe lit another cigarette as the drizzle became a downpour. He trembled, cursing his luck. It would have to rain, today of all days, the day he was ready to break out.

Suddenly a small green Morris van turned ponderously into the street. Joe stepped from the pavement and flagged it down. This was it. He couldn't stop now. His heart leapt wildly as the van shuddered to a halt.

'What's up, Joe?' asked Old Man Johnstone, poking his head through the open window. 'Need a lift?'

Joe wanted to turn and run, but it was too late. He snapped into action. 'Yes please, Mr Johnstone. The hooter's already gone.'

'I don't know, you young 'uns,' chuckled

Johnstone, opening the passenger door. Joe ducked into the car and, pulling a sawn-off shotgun from beneath his jacket, slammed the door.

'I'm sorry, Mr Johnstone,' Joe smiled, pulling the trigger. 'Take that.' Then Joe leaned over the seat and, grabbing the cash box, ran. He knew he would never be able to stop, but he didn't care.

He was out.

He was free.

The End

THE BIRDS 'N THE BEES

'Note the openings on the female body.'

'I sure do, Pa. I'm noticing them all.'

'Well, you'll see them folds of skin around them openings.'

'I sure do, Pa.'

'Good. Squat slightly with your legs apart, son.'

'Like this, Pa?'

'That's right, son. See, any durn fool can use a tampon.'

'Even me, Pa?'

'Even you, son.'

The End

HOLE AHOY!

She came aboard at Liverpool. I saw her straight away. The white flesh of her breasts nudged past me as she made her way to her cabin.

I was young, hard and full of meat, and she was the first woman I'd seen in four years.

Later that night we put out for the Cape and nothing was seen of our passenger for the next two months.

Next thing I knew I was hot, wet and on deck – so was she! From the poop I could see her bending over the rail, the wind flattening her skirt against the curves of her buttocks and thighs. My sheath tightened.

Fore and aft the men began to fight.

Just then, the Cap'n rushed on deck and fired his pistol into a bloke. **'AVAST!'** he raged. **'BELAY THERE, SHIP SHITE! THERE'S ONLY ONE**

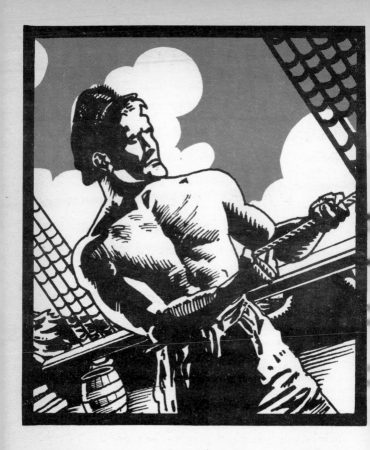

TYPE OF SEAMEN I WANT ON THIS DECK, AND THAT'S MINE!'

Just then he turned on me. He seemed ready to kill me, to bite me in half, when, suddenly, a cry came from aloft.

'HURRICANE OFF THE PORT BOW, CAP'N!'

All hands turned as one to see the angry, black clouds storming on the horizon. Plus! Angry, white lightning crackling within them.

'BRAIL THE SPANKER! ALL HANDS ALOFT!' roared the Cap'n. **'WENCH! To thy BUNK!'**

The halliards were vasted, the fo'c'sles bolted, and the ship made ready for the wind, when, suddenly, the main mast collapsed and squashed the skipper flat as a mackerel.

All hands went mad.

She leapt from the poop and grabbed me. She pushed me to her cabin and slammed the door. She stood there breathing. We both did. Outside the waves began to lash into the ship. It had begun to get very hot when the front of her dress burst open.

For a moment everything seemed still. The crashing of the sea; the thunder in the sails; the rumble of the storm. I could see her eyes. With mine.

'Lady!' I snarled, hardening. 'The Cap'n's dead!'

'So what?' she gasped. 'You're Cap'n now!' With that she threw her arms around me and slobbered wetly along my neck. I tried to push her off, but she bore me back on a bunk. 'Suck me!' she panted. 'There!'

Afterwards, we both lay there and stank.

The End

THE GRINDER AND THE WHIRLWIND

Thunk! Click! PLOP!
cough!
Thunk! Thump! click!
clap!
'Cliff Thorburn one. Jimmy White
to play.'
THWAACK!!!
PLOP! PLOP! PLOP! PLOP!
GASP!!!
cough!
squeaksqueaksqueak
THWAAACK!!!
THUNK! THUNK! THUNK! Thunk!
      thunk!   thu-
nk!
click!

rattle!
PLOP!
GASP!!!
cough!
squeaksqueaksqueak
THWAAACK!!!
SMAAACK!!!
PLONK!!!
GASP!!!
CLAP!!!
cough!
'Frame to Jimmy White.'

The End

VIC!

Before he croaked I gave him the works.
Gun. Fist. Foot. Bollocks. The lot. Then I

shoved him in a ditch and planted him. 'Happy Christmas, Jim,' I rasped, laughing, and left.

Back in the heap I was feeling pretty crazy. Like I needed a drink bad. I gunned the Thunderbird down to Santa Monica and hit a bar called Harry's.

It was a dump.

Harry was fat. Had two arms, one eye, and a mouth that spat a lot. I was all ready to knock him out when the redhead showed up.

She was six-two in her heels, pale, thin and white-lipped.

She breezed over. Took a slug at the bottle of J.D. and smiled. Jeez, I coulda killed a kid, she was that cute.

She gave me the once over. 'Six-eight. Ugly. Crumpled suit. Low forehead. You must be Vic Bicep. Private eye.'

I smashed my head, wet my knickers and bit a bar stool on the leg. When I was through with that I took my head off and banged it on the wall.

Later, when it was done, I hit a Tex-Mex chilli bar called Gu-ba's.

It was a dump.

I was into my third bottle when the Feds cruised in. They wore Dakron slacks and jackets, bakelite hearing aids and a brace of Remmy riot rifles. I didn't think they were kidding when they asked me outside.

But that was five years ago. These days I'm just another convict on Death Row.

Bald. Bummed. And bored.

The End

he PIG

Gunter exploded into the barn. 'What in the hail's goin' on here?!'

Suddenly, Bob stopped.

Gunter loomed over the pig and poked it with his foot. 'This here hog's as dead as . . .

as...' Gunter didn't rightly know what it was as dead as, but when he kicked it again he knew that it was dead. 'Is this pig dead?'

Bob turned his back on the pig so as not to meet its eyes. 'I just came in here and there it was. It's like that sometimes. I come in here and there it is.'

'You mean to say that this here pig's been here before?' the Preacher said in astonishment.

'It kinda looks that way, Preacher, though I wouldn't have known it myself if you hadn't a said.'

'Well I'll be gosh-danged and shagged by a bullet-proof mongoose!' Gunter said looking at Bob. 'I never know'd there was a pig in here before.' Gunter wiped the sweat from his neck and, hitching-up his duds, saw a bottle between Bob's feet. 'Well I'll be a ten foot racoon Bob, ain't that your bottle there?'

'Sure as hail is.'

Gunter took the bottle and drank it. Then he got down and rolled on the pig. The

Preacher came over and looked at them. Then he looked at the empty bottle. Beads of sweat erupted on his head like balloons. Then he looked at the pig again for a long time.

'See anything?' asked Gunter.

'Not much,' sulked the Preacher. 'Just that goddam pig and that there empty bottle what you done gone and emptied.'

'Why, Preacher,' laughed Bob, catapulting to his feet. 'That there ain't the only bottle in this here barn.'

Bob slid a crate from under a bale of straw and took a bottle from it. 'It's all here, Preacher!'

While Bob and the Preacher were drinking from the crate, Gunter got to his feet and looked at the pig. He stood there and looked at it for a long time. Then he leaped back.

'Did you see that pig move just then?!' he shouted, startled.

'Not much,' said Bob. 'Here, here's a bottle that's nearly full.'

Gunter looked at the pig. There was nothing much to see but the flesh. There was the snout and the trotters and the tail, but apart from that it was mostly just like any other pig. Yet still Gunter gazed at the hog as if he'd never seen one in his whole life.

The Preacher turned round and kicked Gunter in the back. 'Why don't you move over and give a man of the cloth a look?!'

'See anything?' Bob laughed.

The Preacher said nothing. Instead, he pulled the stopper from a fresh bottle and emptied it. Then he wiped the snot from his nose with a spare finger. After that he didn't do nothing much but look at the pig.

'See anything, Preacher?' Bob rolled on his back and creased up with laughter when, suddenly, Gunter erupted.

'I swear to God I just seen that goddam pig move!'

Bob froze and, handing Gunter a bottle, stood up to take a look. After he'd finished he drank another bottle and broke the

empty on the pig's head. 'That there pig's as dead as... as...' Bob didn't know just what it was as dead as, but he knew it was dead. 'It ain't nothing much but a dead pig anyhows.'

Gunter opened another bottle. 'I knows it's bound to look just like it did the last time, but I just can't stop looking at that dead pig.'

The Preacher began to pace nervously around the barn. He didn't stop until he was close to God. 'Don't gawk so. You'd better let a man of God take a look once in a while.'

Gunter fell over, bottleless. 'Sure is damned hot,' he drawled. 'Makes a man wanna empty bottles all day long.'

'Sweet Jesus,' gasped the Preacher. 'I don't know nothing I like looking at more than a dead pig. Just like that one there.' Then, he adjusted his eye to check.

Just then Gunter catapulted to his feet. 'I've got a dong on me that'd choke a three ton muskrat!'

'Quit yakkin' on so, Gunter,' Bob spat, disgusted. Then he took a Jew's harp from his pocket and began to play.

The Preacher kept time with his feet.

'That there's the best dead pig in the whole world,' roared Gunter. 'Even if it is still alive!'

'That there pig ain't livin' no more'n a lynched cowpoke,' said Bob, removing the harp from his mouth. 'Why, I come down here most every day and there ain't one gosh-danged whole thing to look at but that there pig. It's the most gosh-danged thing to look at though.'

Gunter fell over again.

'It ain't nuthin' but a dead pig,' Bob went on, laughing. 'But I'll be damned if it ain't just the most interesting thing. You kinda just glance at it and then, before you even know'd it, you can't take your eyes off it. Even if it don't move none, you just don't wanna take your eyes off it.'

Bob put the Jew's harp back in his mouth and began to play. After a while he was playing like he was crazed and there weren't no stopping him until God gave him his last breath.

Gunter was drinking as much as he could manage of anything he found. But he couldn't take his eyes off the pig. Every once in a while he'd jump to his feet and swear that the pig had moved, or whistled, or rolled a cigarette or something. But it was always while the others weren't watching and they didn't believe him.

'Look at old Gunter there,' the Preacher

shouted. 'He just can't get his eyes off that pig!' Then the Preacher kicked Gunter heavily in the ribs. 'Shove off Gunter,' he boomed. 'Let the eye of God get in there a while.'

Just then Gunter began to cry. 'I could look at that there pig till I died. There's something about that pig that makes me wanna... wanna...' Gunter didn't rightly

know what it was that he wanted, only that he didn't know what it was. But, he consoled himself, at least it was something.

Bob was playing like Satan himself. He was twanging away till he was near dead, but he just could not stop. Finally, his finger fell off and the barn filled up with silence.

Gunter began to cry again. 'If I could just look at that there pig 'nd it was a woman I reckon I'd be . . . be . . .' Gunter didn't rightly know what he'd be, only that he'd be something.

The End

THE PARABLE

'This is a fish!' spat Christ.

'Giz it!' roared the mob.

'Listen!' he said, his wallet billowing heroically in the breeze. 'There was a job. And unto it came lads in their millions. And they said unto it, "HUH!"'

**Suddenly, there was a plague!
So. There was just one job, and God got it.**

The End

THE DIARY OF A DEVELOPING WEREWOLF

It all started when I was a pup...

May 29th:
Full moon. Stayed in shaving. Running out of blades fast!

May 30th:
Barked!

The End

PUB ACTION!

Just then a bloke erupted into the snug with a fiver. The music stopped. Jaws dropped, and darts hung in mid-air. **'DRINKS ALL ROUND!'** he roared. **'FOR ME!'**

I ran up and kicked him with all I had in the head. Then, I got down on my knees and, butting him in the stonks, tore off his ears.

He screamed when I bit him twice on the

eyes, and he screamed a whole lot more when I spat them back at him. After that I ripped out a beer and drank it. Then, when I'd done that, I turned him over and punched his bum in. I bent over and was grabbing his fiver when I saw a note hidden on the deck in front of me: 'meet me back at the flat for smack and that'.

Panting, I dragged the gleaming, slug-packed **MAC** slowly from its leather harness. After that, I let two dozen slugs into him. Then, I lit a fag, kicked him in the heart a few times, and left.

Later, at the address there, I unveil a vicious little Israeli machine-pistol and cock it. I counted to one and exploded into the dump.

Six junkies shit for the first time in six months. I smelled the food they hadn't ate. I felt the hate surge through me like a tidal wave of venom. I saw the poverty and wrenched unnaturally.

Just then the gun went off accidently in my hand.

Ugly slugs cut ugly lumps from ugly punks leaving ugly wounds.

I puked up in a pram full of smack.

Next, a bloke sprang into the room with a gun. He pointed it at me. Then he went, 'You've puked on my smack! Take that!' and shot me.

He kept on shooting me till he was out of slugs, and that's when I got **MAD!**

I leaned over and, punching my arm up him, grabbed his tongue and quickly pulled him inside-out. The sleeve of my Tacchini track suit top was fucked. But it was worth it!

The End

GREASEBY

At two in the morning on September twenty-first precisely, Jack Hammer sagged into his twenty-third pint at the bar of the Ale Strangler on Lager Lane.

He and Noska had managed, by murderous methods, to wangle the night out together and, not being the type of lads for the peace and quiet of some mere cafe, had plumped for the illegal, after hours session at the infamous Ale Strangler. Noska had a mate that he'd robbed a lot of money from, so dosh was no problem. However, there were other drawbacks...

'Oi!' Jack jeered and, urinating where he stood, ordered four more lagers, each. 'How come der's no talent in dis dump?! Where's all de birds?!'

'All de best one's are shagging right now,' Noska sulked, ordering another half dozen pints. 'It's two-thirty in the morning.'

Jack watched a fight in the corner and

was glad that they'd gone out, but the shortage of women bothered him. So, it was with some relief that they annihilated their thirty-second pint and left.

The rest of the night was just as frustrating, and it was with sheer relief that Jack paid the fiver for a gobble from an old bag on the promenade.

Suddenly, a copper appeared from out of the blue. 'I think I'm right in saying,' he said, 'that you are gobbling that man.'

'No,' said the old bag.

'Why not?!' Noska yelled loudly and head-butted the old bag on the nose.

'That was brave, lad,' said the copper. 'What made you do it?'

'Well,' said Noska. 'I thought I might put my foot in it, but then I decided to use my head.'

'Very bright,' said the copper. 'Very bright indeed.'

The End

THE WILD WEST

BANG!!!
Gunshot!
BANG!!! BANG!!!
Two shots.
BANG!!! BANG!!! BANG!!!
'Your gun's empty, Ringo. Get out of town!'
'Nope!'

The End

THE VIKINGS!

Meat on the table. Women dancing. Tankards bursting with ale. The smell of roasting meat. The sound of a thousand voices raised in song. The taste of victory in every mouth. **VIKINGS!**

Chief Thor Hammer the Mad quaffed back a horn of Nordic proportions and punched a Swede in the head. He surged to his feet, a powerful oath on his lips:

'**WENCH!!!**' he roared. 'A horn of Bjornborger for a Viking Warlord!'

Suddenly, from amongst the Northern Horde, a leather-clad warrior lurched boldly to his feet. 'Raiders!' he cried, his long blonde hair on his head. 'I be Chief Orsonberg the Official from the Fjord Estate, raise with me your horns in honour of our leader in battle this day, the great War chieftain Thor Hammer the Mad, who has laid on all our beer and **SKÜT!**'

The mighty, blood-spattered Vikings roared their approval and punched each other.

Thor Hammer the Mad threw back his head and howled: 'Today we have won a great victory for the Viking race! We have burst the Brits! Slashed the Saxons! Punched the Picts! Robbed the Romans and gobbed the Gauls!!'

Just then Eric the Red walked in and said, casually, 'Guess what I've just found?!'

'**WHAT?!!!**' roared the wolf-pack.

'America.'

'**YOINKS!!!**' roared the wolf-pack again, their horns aloft. '**SKÜT!!!**'

The End

THE EARTH AND THE SOIL

IT'D been four years since the last rain and Wolfgang now surveyed his land. For a thousand acres it spread before him: dry, barren, lifeless. The sun beat heavy upon him from its scorching blue ocean.

Wolfgang shifted in the dust and made his way back to the shack. He'd been on this land for twenty-four years. He'd fought Indians, range warriors and governments, but nothing could drive Wolfgang from the land his father had died for. Nothing, that is, except drought.

Ute had packed her bag early in the morning. She couldn't sleep. The unbearable heat and the knowledge of their leaving had kept her awake. She'd busied herself with woman's things.

'Tis time, woman.'

'Aye.'

They stood for some time in the door looking back.

Times.

Aye . . .

*   *   *

Two years later Wolfgang was nicely settled in a small town north of the desert. He had a job as mechanic in a garage, and Wolfgang thrived at the chance to blacken his hands.

Ute too was happy. For Ute was with child. Daily she bustled about the hut that they rented from the garage owner with an unnatural velocity.

Wolfgang had crafted a small cot from an orange box, and Ute saw to it that the straw was fresh every day. She did it because of her nerves. But Wolfgang didn't mind. If she be happy, thought he, then so be I.

The day Ute had the baby Wolfgang had

been working on one of the new model
Ford's at the garage. The owner was a
plump wealthy-man, with a cheery, red
face and bright sparkling eyes. He seemed
very pleased at Wolfgang's joy.

'Tis a fine stout lad the wife has had
then, Wolf?'

'Aye, sir. A farmer!'

The fat man stared at Wolfgang's hare lip, his withered arm. 'I be pleased for thee Wolfgang, lad. For I know that thou dost love thy wife very much. But tell me, would it not be sinful to raise the lad in that oily little hut that thou dost inhabit?'

'I've not given it much thought, sire. To be true, I canst think of naught but motors.'

'Aye lad, I know it. But thou must always remember, Wolfgang, you can't beat the **POTATO!**'

OFFICIAL!

PICK-UP!

Dick Champion ran a bath and got in it.

'**WASH!**' he roared to himself.

Later, he saw himself in a mirror. He was slick, stiff and hard. He rubbed himself with a shirt. '**CHRIST!**' he went. 'I'm not **POSH!**' Which was tight really, because he'd always wanted a class bird to squirt...

Debbie Tracy had a job in Skyplunge Executive Parking, but at night she was different. She had fashion. She had hairspray. She had make-up.

Later, she drooled at a bloke in a mag and wept. 'I wish I was **POSH!'** She whimpered. Which was tight really, because she'd often wondered if she'd ever get squirted by a rich bloke...

*   *   *

That night at the Pub n'Club there were a lot of Yobs. They drank. They shouted. They did both. When a bird came in they went, **'SNORKYERTWATLUV?!'** and that.

Dick drank a pint. He drank four. Then he saw Cheryl and slid over.

'Shag?!' he announced casually over the **WHAM!**

'Sorry, Dick. I'm on the **BLOB!'** Cheryl roared, tits and fag dangling.

Suddenly, Debbie Tracy raced onto a

bus and got there. Her dress was on. Her make-up was too. She'd had a hair do. She'd had ten!

She paid the bloke a quid and met a mate. They figged a bit and then lagered. After that her mate, Pat, figured, 'I wouldn't suck a bloke's knob for nowt!'

'I would!' Debs smirked brazenly. 'Twice!'

'YAK!' spat Pat. 'Them tonkies taste 'orrible!'

Just then Dick Champion sauntered back from the bog. Never before had he been reduced to such blagging. He'd asked a bird for a squirt. He'd asked the lot! He felt a fool. Then, he felt another. He was pissed. He was lagered. He was both. But on hearing a slowy, he made a final heroic effort and plunged wearily back onto the dance-floor.

'Oo, look at that!' directed Pat. Suddenly Debs knew that here was a man who, she hoped, would, before the night was through, rampantly and without recourse to savagery, squirt her!

'RUT?!' Dick asked, his neckwear tightening.

'After' she replied, hardly figging.

They danced. Then they danced some more. Later, they snogged, cabbed, curried, biffed and squirted.

Next morning she woke-up, tasted a tonky, and left.

The End

SCAB!

'It's **OFFICIAL!!!** We're **OUT!!!**'
'You're **SACKED!!!**' roared the boss, calling up the cops. '**STOP THAT LOT!!!**'
When I got to the pit it was shut. The route was lined with cops. My mates and me were mad. I ripped out a cosh and barked, '**LADS!!! FIGHT BACK!!!**'

A cop surged forward picket-punching. I lashed out and dropped him. Then, leaping over his body, I stopped a bus. 'It's the **SCABS** from Job-U-Rob!' I roared, as the cops charged at us. 'Let's get 'em!'

'He's right!' piped a picket. 'Let's burst the bus with bricks!'

'Yeah!' cried another. 'What's a ballot?!'

Then, the lads smashed the cab and, tearing it open, dragged out the scabs. The pigs piled in, but we were ready. We'd worked in the dark for this. We were pit-hardened steel and desperate for work. The odds were with us. The people behind us.

But, without the support of any other Union, we lost!

The End

PAC-MEN!

WANTED!
P.A.C. – MEN!
The Pub Action Committee
NEEDS YOU!
Enrol Today!

Noska lethargically observed the poster in the Job Shop Window. 'PUB ACTION?' he thought. 'Sounds good.' So he went to the building where auditions were being held.

There was a long line of lads when he got there, but finally a bloke shouted, 'Next!' and it was his go. 'Name?!'

'Noska,' he said, his cap off.

'Address?!'

'Cattle Rock Squat.'

'Age?!'

'Constantly.'

'Right then!' the bloke, a vulturesque fellow with two bright yellow fingers, said.

'We are the Pub Action Committee and we're on the look out for good, war-waging commandos for our squad. We're brutal, messy, cruel and vengeful. But we're fair. We have to be. We're talking ALCOHOL!'

Noska snapped to attention.

'Recently,' the bloke continued, 'we've been getting reports of certain people not drinking. If this were ever to get out, for example, to the enemy...' He tapped his substantial nose with a yellow finger.

'My god!' roared Noska. 'Unthinkable!'

'Exactly, my boy! We must get these people away from the T.V. and BACK INTO THE PUBS!!! Are you with us, lad?!'

'Aye!' he said, grabbing a pen. 'Let's make it **OFFICIAL!**'

*   *   *

Madge and Arthur Scoggley were sitting watching 'Win the Wife' after their supper. He was a night watchman on day-shifts. She was a pensioner on Mogadon.

'Our Noska's late tonight, luv,' creaked Arthur, eyes fixed to the telly.

'Probably out with his mates,' Madge sighed, knitting.

*   *   *

Noska's neck pumped as he sat crouched and ready in the back of the van. Around him were sixteen of his mates: hand-picked, tough and dedicated to the spread of Worldwide Alcoholism. He'd often heard of people not drinking. Even his father, a man close to his heart, had sometimes refrained from imbibing the Hallowed Mead. If ever the lads were to find out...

'Right men!' barked the Squad Commander, resplendent in his Kronenbourg Combat Kit. 'Let's get out there! If anyone resists, subdue him and administer this!' He lifted a half-gallon flagon. 'This is pure spirit, Gold Label and Scrumpy! After that they'll be racing you to the Ale Strangler!

With that the P.A.C.-men burst out of the van and down the street, breaking off into packs of two to knock at slacker's doors.

Noska and his mate caught a mob of squatters who put up a good fight until they were subdued and put to the flagon. Soon, just as the Commander had said, they put on their ceremonial Blackthorn Aprons and disappeared in the direction of the Pub.

Job done, the two heroes ambled back to the van where a crowd had gathered around an old couple.

'These two buggers refuse to drink!'

growled a P.A.C.-man, gripping the old man by the neck. 'They will be interned in a Toxification Camp until their blood count returns to normal!'

As Noska drew up, a wave of fear and compassion washed over him as he recognised the pensioners in question.

'Mum! Dad!' he croaked. 'OH NO!'

Noska's parents were later committed to a new anti-TV wing at the centre, while he was jailed for conspiring with known health freaks.

The End

THE FIGHT!

The mob piled in. Heat. Sweat. Noise. Smoke.

The **FIGHT!** Stripped to the waist they clashed; local lads locked in combat!

Mallet spat blood, trod back, ducked, and blasted into Gunter's neck. **THUD!**

Gunter took it and roared back like a tank! **THUD! CRUNCH! SMACK!**

Mallet hit the deck! **SPLAT!**

Mallet snored! **ZZZZ! DING!** Saved by the bell!

A wet rag slapped his map. 'Come on kid!' barked his boss. 'We need that cash for meat and that! Do 'im!'

Mallet launched a brutal attack!

Gunter caught a savage clout. **THWACK!** And dropped!

'... Seven... Eight... Nine... TEN!' **OUT!**

And that was that!

The End

THE ELECTION

The pig trundled mindlessly into the room. Then, trundled out again...

Meanwhile, on the porch, Gunter was sheltering from the sweltering heat when Sheriff Big Jack McCloud rode up and yelled, 'Howdy, voter!'

'Sure is a fine day for the Lord's heat, Sheriff,' rocked Gunter, jetting a stream of tobacco at the law's horse.

'Why hay thar, pig farmer,' the Sheriff drawled. 'I rode on out here t'make sure y'all gonna vote come Friday.'

'Why, I'd jest luv to, Sheriff, but I've got a mighty sick pig here needs a spoon feedin', an' if I leave him for to long I gits to frettin'.'

'Things jest won't be the same without your vote, Gunter,' the Sheriff urged, urgently. 'Seems to me like you should jest pick up that there hawg an' take it into town with you.'

'Can my pig vote, too?'

'Sure can, neighbour. I need all the votes I kin git.'

'No shit?!' went Gunter, astonished. 'I'll do it!'

*   *   *

Gunter's battered, black, dust-covered Ford rattled down Main Street and jerked violently to a halt. The streets were crammed with ale-strangling Georgia folk gripped in the heat of election fever. Guns went off and the sound of frantic piano playing blasted from the saloon.

Gunter licked his lip and, picking up the stricken pig, bolted through the bat-wings into the blood-splattered bar of The Malamute Saloon.

The bar was crammed with cow-punching, whisky-drinking, poker-playing shitkickers. Loose women in scarlet sprawled profitably on pleasure-seeking politicians, and free-spending tin miners staked fortunes on the spin of a crooked roulette wheel.

'My, my,' Gunter thought, sweating. 'I think I'll git me a beer. I sure could drink a whole shitload after all that danged fancy auto-mobilin'.'

Suddenly, the pig brightened when a large-scale, wide-spread saloon girl approached them behind the breathtaking view of her colossal, worldbeating chests. 'Hi there, voter. Like to buy lil' ol' me a drink?'

'I sure would miss,' drawled Gunter, shouldering the pig. 'But I got me here this sick pig needs a suckling, but it sure looks to me like you could feed a whole shitload.'

Just then Dangerous Kid Cruelty roamed up usefully. 'No woman a mine is gonna suckle no goddam sick pig, boy,' he warned, levelling the gaping black tunnel of the six-shooter at Gunter's pig. 'So git outta here!'

'You can rape ma wife and kids. You can burn ma farm an' chop ma chickens, but don't never point a gun at ma pig,' drooled Gunter. Then he stepped back and, checking his weight, launched a bloke-stopping poke to the kid's brains and killed him.

'I like a man with spunk!' the saloon girl jutted, territorially. 'Buckets of it. Why don't we go up to my room and fool around?'

'Goddam it, miss, I'd jest luv to,' Gunter drawled, fingering the pig. 'But I got a mighty sick-looking hawg needs a fondlin', an' if I leave him for too long I gits to frettin'.'

'Why don't y'all jest pick up that there hawg and bring it up with you?'

'You mean ma pig can come, too?'

'Sure can, pig farmer. He's old enough to vote, ain't he?'

'No shit?!' went Gunter, astonished. 'I'll do it!'

The End

THE ANGLER!

plop

The End

JOB!

Then, suddenly, I burst down a long, dimlit door-lined corridor and, exploding into one, erupted into the vast wetness of her limitless breasts and stopped. Hardening, I jabbed the MAC into her ribs and spat, 'GET NAKED!'

We did it.

Just then Kid Colt burst in. 'GET BACK!' he barked, twin pistols packed. 'THAT'S MY GASH YOU'VE SNATCHED!'

FLASH!!! I ATTACKED!!!

BUT! She stepped back and **CRACK!** It went black.

* * *

'Mallet?'

'WHAT?!' I asked, aching. Then, I saw her! The sheer vital tonnage of her and I leapt to my feet.

Kid Colt charged in spurting lead. I copped one in the neck and laughed.

'YOU'VE MADE ME MAD!' I roared, wounded.

He'd blown off the lot and his gat was blank when I got him. Jetting, I drove my fist straight through his stomach wall and, grinning, ripped his liver from his body, loudly.

'YOU WON'T BE NEEDING THAT WHERE YOU'RE GOING!' I spat and, cramming his body into the toilet pan, pulled the chain. Then, MAC out, I blast her. She burst back dead and stopped. Boosted, I hit a pub and, laughing, drank it.

JOB DONE!

The End

WORMWOOD

ONCE upon a pint there was a dump called Wormwood and **ELVIS, THUD** and **ROCKWOOD THUG** were in it. Suddenly, they escaped, but were grassed, framed, trapped, set-up, bribed, bummed and banged up again.

ONE day, **THUD THUG** was on the bog exercising when Officer Droppam burst in. 'Oi!' he screamed confidentially. 'Your kid **ROCKWOOD** is going gay!'

'YOINKS!' roared Thud attractively. 'Our kid a fag!'

'That's right. So fill your pot and get 'im!'

Meanwhile, on Z-wing, **ELVIS THUG** and **BOX DUPALOTT** were laughing at nowt when Mac le Beast roamed up. 'Need a fist-fuck, chuck?' he said in French.

'Not now. Not never. Not with you. No.' rasped **BOX**.

'Yeah, beat it,' spat **ELVIS**.

'Ah, come on, fellas,' pled Mac le Beast. 'Give a cock a home.'

'I wouldn't give your cock a biscuit,' barked **BOX** brutally. 'I wouldn't give your cock the pleasure of savage brutality!'

'Me neither,' slurred **ELVIS** in his characteristically Bavarian accent that amazed felons and fugitives alike. 'So fuck off!'

'You think you are sole good with your tight little bottoms and your Viking manners. So why don't you sit on the toilet? Why don't you play your draughts and dominoes? I know plenty that like a good bum punch! That ROCKWOOD twat for one!'

'Are you calling his kid a turd burglar?' BOX burst.

'Oui.'

'You're a fucking liar,' ELVIS tightened unnaturally. He felt the heat of the gas burn on his neck. He smelt the smell of a thousand stinking pots. He heard the inhuman cries of five thousand condemned men. He tasted the beer that wasn't there. He saw the sweaty, frightened face of Mac le Beast and laughed. 'Prove it!'

'You bet I can. Only zis morning zat Chinese kid, Bum Funn Chum, sez 'e was in your bruzzer only las' night.'

Just then THUD THUG rushed up fast and stopped. Panting, he gasped, 'It's OFFICIAL! He's a glove puppet! Our ROCKWOOD is bent!'

That night at slop-out ROCK-

WOOD THUG was in a bloke when Officers Ripemoff, Feelham and Petit and Governors Stripham, Wetham and Shaggam walked miraculously in. 'What's up?!' roared Wetham, his suit on.

'I am! Apparently.' **ROCKWOOD** felt bum-hole-grip-in-fear.

'You've bummed that lad!' Shaggam shouted, his hard on.

'Twice,' laughed **ROCKWOOD THUG**. 'Look!'

'You offal-robbing bum-bandit!' splut-

tered Officer Ripemoff. 'Get your gut off that lad's back!'

Suddenly THUD THUG and ELVIS THUG burst out from nowhere, accompanied by an intrepid stench.

'What's ROCKWOOD got?!' they said.

'A fat lad, that's what!'

'What's that on our kid's cock?!'

'The fat lad's bum.'

'A fat lad?! In Wormwood?!'

Just then Officer Ripemoff got stuck up and went: 'Come on men, there's meat for all. Plenty of it.'

'Yoinks!' howled a screw. 'He's right!'

And that's how the fat lad got bummed flat in Wormwood nick.

OFFICIAL!!!

DAY OF THE DOG

I was in me basket when I woke up. I yawned and looked about. There was a space in me bowl where food should be. As usual. I got up and shook. Then I had a sniff at this and that. Then the doorbell rang. So I went out and barked a bit. The big one came down, clouted me, and let in a bird. I got me nose in quick, as usual. He kicked me good and proper for that – but it was worth it!

The End

BETWEEN TWO LUNGS

I don't have friends. **GOOD!** Who needs 'em? Not me. The only friend I have is my MAC 10. One point six kilogrammes of instant death. A beauty. A little too bulky for my pocket, that's true, so at work I house a Browning. A war-hog. So, why all the guns? Well, as any D.H.S.S. Fraud Investigator will tell you, it's getting awful rough on the streets.

My name's Mallet. Jim Mallet. People who know me call me Mr. Mallet. I'm a plug-ugly gang if ever there was one. When I was a kid I always wanted a job that'd give me access to other people's homes. True, this job didn't exactly offer the prospect of destroying a lot of exotic locations, but it did have its perks. I get to go into any home I want. Lots of them. Like this one.

This one was a squat above a

tobacconists on Shepherd's Bush Green. I was after a turd called Firth. Julian Firth, the Bishop's son. He was an actor. A bad one. I say 'was' because when I found him he was dead! He was lying on a badly worn Afghan mat with the syringe still hanging from his arm and a big crowd of cops all round him.

'Who called you, Mallet?!'

It was Ford Stockwood. Detective-

Sergeant Stockwood, Homicide. We went back a long way. He was as bent and as crooked as they come. Like me.

'What's the dope, Stockwood?!'

'Ah, nuttin'. Kid popped out on junk, see.'

'So what's wiv de murder boys?! Dirty?!'

'Nah. S'all routine stuff. Know 'im?'

'Sure! The stiff's a ham actor called Julian Firth!'

'Actor, huh?'

'Yeah! Y'listenin'?!'

Stockwood rescued the smokes from their cellophane gaol and flashed. Lighting up he says, 'So why you in?'

'Routine! I heard he found a fiver that he never declared! I don't like that!'

'A fiver?'

'Yeah! Y'listenin' aren't yer?!'

'A lousy fiver? You were muscling the kid for a lousy fiver?'

'So what's lousy about a fiver?! I like fivers! I like all I can get! Besides, who's to say he hadn't done it before?! One day it's a fiver, the next it's a grand!'

'Jesus, Mallet. Your job stinks.'

I filled my fists on the cheap, man-made fabric of his off-the-peg suit and drove my knees into his ribs. 'Listen, copper!' I hissed. 'I don't have to stand here all day and listen to you bad-mouthing the system! The system IS, and that's official! You've got your job and I've got mine! My job's to make sure that the scum don't steal off the people! Evasion of income-tax is a crime! A vicious crime! A crime that drives our Government into the hands of the inter- national money lenders! If all these punks paid-up it'd be another story! And you'd better believe it, Stockwood, when I say I'm here to make them pay! Never forget that!'

I slapped his puffing face with the back of my hand a dozen times or so real fast and then let him have it in the guts. Then I pointed him at the body.

'See that?!' I rasped. 'See that?! That's what dodging the system does for you! How can anyone afford an overdose on three quid a day?! If I could've caught him earlier then maybe he'd still be alive right now!'

I dropped him then and straightened what was left of his suit a bit.

He waved his heavies back with his arm and loosened his tie. There was a gleam of something mad in his eye. 'You're dirty, Mallet. Very dirty. You're as low as they come. Know that? It's you and your likes that drive kids to this.'

'That's crap!' I snarled. 'Rich people take junk, same as anybody! Content yourself with that, sucker! Rich people are as human as you!'

With that I left. When I hit the street it was raining hard. The tarmac had that yellow glow from the overhead street lamps that I usually write about when I'm looking for atmosphere. The traffic was roaring by. There were people all over.

Poor people!
GOOD!

The End

ME, SEAMAN

He crushed his mouth across her shivering flesh.

'Now! Now!' he panted.

Her broad hips writhed against him. He grabbed her. She arched erotically in his hands. 'Love me,' she gasped. 'Love me hard!'

Years later, Wolf gazed out across his ship as it went around the world. **'LAND AHOY!'** shouted a bloke in a basket.

The men, hungry for lust after a two year voyage, fought wildly amongst themselves to get into the boats.

'AVAST! DECK SWABS!' roared Wolf, clouting the stern of an eager young seaman. **'PLUNDER!'**

'Come ashore, cap'n!' cried Jack, the cabin boy.

'Not me, lad. I'll not taste the flesh of native women. Not while I search for **HER!'**

That night, by the light of the burning villages, Wolf stood alone on deck. He cast an empty bottle of rum into the water, the sound of his men's bestial revelry floating across the cool air of the bay, horrifically!

Then, catapulting backwards, he bolted the for'ard fo'c'sle and grabbed the mainbrace. **'PAT!'** he cried. **'HOW LONG MUST I WAIT?!'**

Suddenly, the air smelt soft and womanish, and the memories came flooding back...

The End

THE SUBBUTEO KING

It began!
FLICK OFF!
Flick! Flick! Flick!
FLICK!
GOAL!!!
One–nil!
What a flicker!

The End

NEVER SAY DIE!

Carefully, Jack hurled himself from the cliff brandishing his sabre between his teeth, his tartan headscarf fluttering traditionally in the rushing wind of his rapid descent. He hit the water with a terrifying **SPLASH!**

For a time the sweaty, black-faced crew of the Sea Eagle stared pop-eyed at the point where Jack had vanished. Seconds

passed. Anxious tongues licked thin, cruel lips. The seconds were becoming minutes. Nervous glances charged across the crowded deck like a pack of hunting wolves. Yet still there was no sign of Jack.

''E's gorn!' Hook McFinney broke.

Then, as a whisper stole as lightly as a thief across the deck, the water suddenly split white and Jack gushed upward at the stars for air.

A great roaring cheer rent the location as the crew went mad.

'Jack's back!!!'

The End

THE GAMBLER!

'ALASKA!' yelled Grit Bunker. 'I've robbed it! Robbed, raped and plundered it! Just now!'

Just then a card sharp shuffled up and went, 'My name's Block. Block Schwerz. An' this here's ma kin, Pat! Notice the Nordic proportions of her voluminous young planets! So, nuggeteer, cut the deck to win a squeeze of these!'

'Dust for lust, huh?'

Grit looked at Pat. He looked at her eyes. Then he looked at her breasts. He could not take his eyes off her breasts. They wrestled loudly towards him like two eager young sea men.

'Name the game, card crap,' Grit drooled.

Schwerz slithered round and hissed, 'Cut! Highest card gets the lot!'

'What's the stake?!' Grit demanded, his eyes still molesting the buttock-like enormity of her breasts.

'ALASKA... OR THIS!' Block roared, wrenching the flimsy, hot threads of her scanty nightie aside to launch the inexhaustible dimensions of her bust upon them.

Grit fought back the rising stench of his manhood and pondered. After sixty-four winters up the Yukon with nothing but wolves to fuck, Grit was ready to RUT! Furiously! But he knew that if he lost he would have nothing. Could he risk it all for Pat? After all those years?

But now a crowd had gathered round, intent on seeing Grit lose his gold for grunt. 'Go for it, Grit!' They egged. Grit licked his lips greedily. He could not take his eyes off her breasts.

'I'll do it!'

'CUT!' rasped Block Schwerz holding out the deck.

Grit did it!

'It's a three!' someone gasped.

Grit groaned, feeling his wad wilt instantly.

'I've scooped your loot!' Block Schwerz laughed.

'Shut it and cut!' Grit grinned, ripping out his pistol and levelling it at Block's head. 'And you'd better pray that it's a two!'
It was.

The End

BRUTE Thunder stormed at the **PUB!**
Mad with hate! Brute was big and tough.
Like a truck. And he could prove it! Nobody
crossed Brute Thunder without a clout. Not
even Jet Outburst and his lot.

JET Outburst looked up from his pint in fear. Jet had called Brute a **TWAT!** at work. And now his mob could do nowt! It was Jet and Thunder! Two men! To the death! **OFFICIAL!**

BRUTE Thunder burst into the pub with the savage intensity of a **ROCK!** 'OUTBURST! You **TWAT!**' Brute spat. 'I'm no **TWAT!** And that's a fact! Sup that jug and get your gob out here now!'

JET piped his mob. Nowt moved. 'You **SCUM!**' he barked. 'I've no need of thee to **THRASH** that **TWAT!** And I'll use **OWT TO DO IT!**' And with that he smashed his mug on a bloke!

BRUTE Thunder blasted at Jet Outburst with all the unbridled ferocity of a **WARHEAD!!!**

BRUTE blocked a clout but snapped back like a wolf. Jet lashed out a fist of glass. Brute ducked but his snout copped a bit of it.

JET butts out. Brute comes back. Now

it's Jet! Now it's Brute! Jet cops a blow to the neck, and another and another and Brute's on top! He's driving in punch after punch after punch after sickening punch. **WHACK! WHACK! WHACK! WHACK! CAN JET TAKE IT?! OH!** Brute stumbles and **JET COMES BACK LIKE A PARA-TROOP ATTACK!** He bites! He **CUTS! HE MAULS! CRACK!** Oh my word... **PUNCH! LEFT! RIGHT! STRAIGHT LEFT! JAB! JAB! JAB! JAB! UPPER-CUT, HOOK, WHAT A SWIPE!! AND HE'S DOWN! BRUTE THUNDER IS DOWN!! STAMP! KICK! WHAT A SPANKING! WHAT A POUND-ING! THEY'RE AT IT LIKE HAMMERS!!! IT'S A BLOOD-BATH!!! BUT BRUTE'S BACK! HOW DOES HE DO IT?!! HA! THIS MAN CAN TAKE OWT! HE'S A BULL! A MONSTER! A**

FRENZIED SAVAGE THUG!!
HE'S ROARING LIKE A DOG!
HE'S TEARING JET TO
PIECES!! IT'S DISGUSTING!!
AND – THAT'S IT! HIS HEAD
GOES IN! JET GOES DOWN!
THIS IS THE END! HE'LL DO
NOWT AFTER THAT! HIS
LIFE'S SPURTING OUT FROM

A VERY NASTY WOUND IN-DEED. BRUTE THUNDER HAS DONE IT!

BOOT atop the body, Brute howled in **VICTORY!** His head all blood he faced the mob! His gob split in a savage snarl! The mob pulled back, their leader dead!

'I'LL BLOW MY GUNS OFF IF I WANT!' he screamed. 'And you'll do nowt but listen! I have come here this day and laid waste! This carnage, this bloody slaughter of your mate, Jet Outburst, heralds the end of your wrecking activities! . . .

'YOU'RE ABOLISHED!! THIS PUB IS MINE!! And I'll **KILL** to keep it. I'm a one-man fucking slaughterhouse with a thirst for **ACTION!** For devastation, beer and **GRUNT!**

'I can lead you, **LADS!** We can rule the length and breadth of every **PUB IN ENGLAND!!!** For-we-are-**MEN!! MEN OF ENGLAND!!! AND WE LIVE BY ONE LAW AND**

ONE LAW ALONE! AND THAT IS THE LAW OF FANG AND CLUB!!! LIVE BY IT OR DIE!!! ARE YOU WITH ME LADS?!!!'

'OFFICIAL!!!' roared the mob.

The End

MUGVILLE

When I got there they were sleeping. All but Kid Pensioner. He came over and said, 'This is a two horse town, son. And I'm both!'

I took his word for it, and left.

The End

THE REBEL

Ivy strained the fat from the custard and sighed. It was the Lord's fourth portion that morning and she was bored. When she first got her job with God she'd been really excited, but now, after 320 years, her heart had begun to pine for the men of a shipyard or barracks.

'Ivy . . ? Ivy . . ? Iveee?'

She tutted and, casting a casual glance at her untouched lager, picked herself up.

'Here you are, God,' she said, placing the pudding before him.

'Cheers, Ivy love,' God blessed heartily. 'Yer a cracker, even if I did make you meself.'

Ivy blushed and tried to cover her two massive wet breasts with two tiny dry hands.

'Give over, God,' she giggled.

''Ere,' God got serious and, turning the sound down on the television, forgave the

custard for a cigarette. 'Where's that bloody Jesus, then?!'

'God knows.'

Just then God moved in a mysterious way. 'What's got into that lad, he's out all the hours I send!'

Suddenly, Jesus flew in. 'Hi, Dad,' he landed.

'Where the bloody hell have you been?!' asked God.

'Look, I'm sick of your holier-than-thou attitude!' Jesus flapped. 'There was a stay-behind in The Wilderness, so some Romans put me up for the night. Anyway, I'm off to the The Last Supper for a pint with the lads'.

The Lord mumbled and pulled out a sack. 'God's speed?'

'Thanks Dad. I'll need it!'

SNORT!!!

The End

QUACK!

My name's Gore. Doc Gore. N.H.S.S. Surgeon. I like guts. I get them. Miles of them.

One day I cut this bloke's head off for a laugh. His mum went mad. Next day I snatched this kid with a brain tumour. It was great. I wheeled him in for the students.

'WATCH THIS!' I roared and went to work. 'After making the initial incision I will cut, hew, hack and slash a bit. Here! Like this!'

The students cheered as I stabbed, sawed, chopped and trimmed. Then I paused and, lighting a fag, shaved, snipped and clipped a bit.

Just then this girl yelled out, 'Ay, mister! Giz a go!'

'Go 'ead!' I laughed. 'Get stuck in!'

She started off with a good old-fashioned two-handed incision. Then she said, 'Mind if I carve, slice and amputate a bit?'

'Sure!' I waved. 'Go 'ead, love. That's a bloody great wound you've made! Carry on! I'm going to the pub for a shit!'

She was really putting her weight into it when I got back. You could tell because the kid woke up. 'Nurse!' I sniggered. 'Cosh that kid will yer!' She did it. Then I pushed her aside and waded into the NUT.

Boyishly I lopped off the end of his knob and trod on it. Then I got down to business. A quick hack and slash. A little peeling, gouging, beheading and that.

Just then a nurse splashed up and went, 'He's dead, Doctor.'

'Never mind,' I laughed. 'I may have lost a patient but I've made a fucking great hammock!'

The End

It was one of those crazy hot days. The men were on the sidewalk. They were sweating.
   Just then a bus drove up.
   The men watched it.

Then the bus drove off again.

Rut Landscape watched it go. Rut had had a hard life. He'd only been six years old when he saw his entire family die at the wheel of a locomotive. Later, he'd lost a dick in a bathing accident, and it was a wound that had plagued him ever since. Plus, he was hot and lost.

Rut looked away then and drew a frog in the sand with a stick. He was thirsty.

Suddenly, another bus drove up and stopped. A woman got off it and stood looking at the men through the swirling clouds of dust. She could feel the hot sun burning the back of her bare legs.

As one, the men gulped and popped out thick pink tongues that moistened.

She could feel their eyes roaming all over her body, exploring every inch as if she were naked...

Rut's hands clenched convulsively in his pocket. It was Pat!

'Rut Landscape!' she breathed, awesomely.

'Pat Walton!' he gasped. 'Git the hail outta here, Pat Walton. Ain't you broken enough men with your lovin'?'

The men surged noticeably.

'If I know you, Pat Walton, you're up to no good in that thin, breast-hugging cotton dress.'

'It'll be different this time,' Pat panted. '**LOOK!**'

Then, with an horrific ripping sound, the men erupted in a fit of high-spirited antics.

Rut looked. His jaw dropped and a yard of spittle fell on his T-shirt. He could feel the hot desert wind dry the sweat on his back. He could taste the dust in his mouth. It was gritty and hot. A tumbleweed blew across the road ... then blew back again. The veins in his neck and body stood out heroically. He tried to look away, but couldn't. Nervously, he drew a ship in the sand with his stick. He was as puzzled as a possum in a parka.

By now the men were fighting to look at Pat, whose breasts struggled simultaneously to remain within the confines of her thin cotton dress. When she moved her naked thighs squeaked together, the sound of which drove the men to fight all the more.

'I've never cared about that wound of yours, Rut,' she steamed hotly. 'You're the only man that can satisfy a big gal like me!'

At the sound of that the men suddenly stopped fighting. 'Yeah!' they shouted, throwing their hats in the air. 'But there's ten of us!'

Quickly, Rut drew a fork in the sand with his stick.

'Who in the hail's he, anyways?' one of the men yelled, surging forward. 'Why, he ain't no more use than a spotted hog in a Goober tree!'

'Yeah!' roared the men. 'Let's lynch him!'

They did it. Then they grabbed Pat.

Later, the last bus drove up and stopped. Pat got on it and left. The men were on the sidewalk. They were sweating. It was one of those crazy hot days.

The End

THE PLOT!

WHACK!!!
I ATTACK!!!

The End

PUB HAWK!

Suddenly, Wing Commander Tom Wallasey sprang into the mess. **'IT'S WAR!!!'** he screamed in upper class.

The men mumbled and stirred in their goggles, their scarves dangling heroically in their beer.

Quickly, I stuffed back a lager field and lurched boldly onto the bar. **'LADS! PIES PUBS and PINTS!! Then SCRAMBLE!!!'**

We did it!

Ten planes took off. Magnificently, we flew them up. While I was driving I ripped out a bottle of scotch, tore the head off, and plugged it in. **'AAAAH!'** I went. **'COMBAT!'**

Then, when I woke up, there were Fokkers everywhere. **'SHIT!'** I screamed and put my foot down. Lead hit my cockpit. I plunged into a cloud. The Fokkers plunged after me. I dove over Dover, flew over

France, and landed in London for lunch, but I couldn't shake them off.

Back in the sky they were driving around all over the place. Later, I got fed up and crashed.

When I woke up I was being punched in the head quarters of the German Army. They wanted my name, rank and number. They got them. **FAST!** Then, the one with the beer opened a bag and took out a leg. My leg. I could tell by the cock at the top.

What they did to my other leg is enough to make the hairs in your pint stand up.

The End

GRAILWOOD

Our story begins long ago, in the Northland, where be Grailwood. Legend has it that every man had his own pub and women cooked daily.

The End

THE LEGEND OF PAUL DIAMOND

Paul Diamond was a girl's best friend – and he knew it! He had a big knob and could go on for hours. He was an athlete. A young God.

Tina Pearson loved fashion. Any fashion. She wore Chelsea Girl tops, read Titbits and listened to Radio One. But she had problems. She couldn't rut!

They met at a stomach-pumping party on the Costa Living in Spain. Henry Cooper presented the first prize of one million pints of Pig Lager to them both.

Suddenly, they'd drunk them!

Paul cast a glance at her gob and belched triumphantly. 'I'm gutted! Fancy a curry?!'

'Not half!' she screamed horrifically, hurling herself backward and exposing herself in mid-air.

'Get naked!!!'

'What kind of girl do you think I am?' she asked, landing loudly.

'Look, I've got a wicket of elephantine proportions and I can go on for hours,' he loomed gloomily.

His eyes looked at hers. Her eyes looked at his. Their eyes looked at each other. It was hot. They were sweating. The sea was coming in... then going out again. In the distance they could hear music. Distant music. They sweated some more. The sand was hot and dry. They were young and drunk. Her mouth was damp and wet. Wet and damp. It was both.

'I have problems with my orgasm!' she gasped. 'I don't have them. I can't! I won't! I never will! **NEVER! NEVER! NEVER! EVER!'** She erupted into a fit of tears and fell into his arms.

'My name is Paul Diamond,' he wavered nostalgically, indicating the agricultural proportions of his swimwear. 'And I'm a girl's best friend.'

It was still hot. Somewhere a bus went past. A dog barked. A pub opened. They were sweating.

He lowered her to the sand. 'Paul,' she groaned realistically.

'Yup.'

'Make me come!'

His swimwear wrenched brutally.

She touched him. He touched her. They were touching each other.

'Oh Paul!' she writhed unnaturally. 'Say you love me. You do love me, don't you?'

His sideboards tightened. He narrowed his eyes into slits. Clenched his fists. His mouth opened wide. His legs bent. His toes knotted.

'Marry me?'

SQUIRT!!!

Just then he woke up. He was still on a bus. He was going to work. It was Monday. It was raining. The streets were crammed with people. Wet people. When he woke up again he was at work. He woke up again at the pub. Then at the match. Finally he woke up at home.

Tina was sprawling rampantly in her pink baby-doll nightdress eating chocolate with her bare hands. There was chocolate on her breasts. On her thighs.

There was chocolate on the tap. There was chocolate outside. Beside her, twelve cans of **Pig Lager** lay crushed next to a damp drainpipe.

Just then he collapsed in general squalor and roared, 'At least I've still got my memories!'

The End